© 2011, 2010, 2006 by
YouthLight, Inc.
Chapin, SC 29036

Project Layout by Amy Rule
Project Editing by Susan Bowman

ISBN 1-59850-007-4

Library of Congress
2005938409

10 9 8 7 6 5 4 3
Printed in the United States of America

P.O. Box 115
Chapin, SC 29036
(800) 209-9774
Fax: (803) 345-0888
www.youthlightbooks.com

About the Authors

Sandy Ragona, MSEd, is an elementary school counselor at J.F. Kennedy School in Dubuque, Iowa with 25 years experience in school counseling. Sandy has been an adjunct professor for Loras College, Drake University, and Morningside College all in Iowa. She has led numerous workshops and training sessions locally and nationally. She is the author of the book "Eliminating Bullying" and co-author of the book "Early Intervention" by Jerry Conrath.

Amy Tranel, is a prevention educator in Dubuque, Iowa. She has been educating children for the past two years. She is currently earning her Masters of Science in Counselor Education at the University of Wisconsin-Platteville. Amy's passion and enthusiasm for working with children will make her an outstanding school counselor.

Dedication

This book is dedicated to our children and to the belief that all children have the right to live in a safe, happy, and healthy environment that promotes the respect and growth of all children.

This book is also dedicated to the adults who educate these children. We have a responsibility to educate ourselves and our children on the issue of bullying, to teach them ways to be respectfully assertive in these difficult situations, and to recognize that we must model the behavior we wish our children to express.

It is our hope that you will read this book and take time to share it with a child you love and respect.

Acknowledgements

I would like to thank Youthlight, Inc. for their support with this book. My heart warmed hugs to my husband, Andy, for his encouragement. To my son, Joe, and his friends, thanks for all the memorable experiences as children.

- Sandy

I would like to thank Sandy, the "Anti-Bullying Guru," for mentoring me through this process and nurturing my passion to make a difference in the lives of children. To Josh, my husband and best friend, and my children, Peyton and Eliana, thank you for your unconditional love and support, for believing in me, and for giving me the courage to take on new adventures. Finally, I would like to thank my parents, Bob and Jayne, for always being there for me when I needed even the slightest of things.

- Amy

"Please Stop, I Don't Like That!"

I Don't Like That!"

6 Magic Words to be Respectfully Assertive

By: Sandy Ragona, M.S.Ed. & Amy Tranel

Illustrated by: Clint Faile

Everyday at Joey's school, the morning recess bell rings at 10:30 am for the first break of the day. Students from all grades put down their pencils, close their books, and line up to go outside. Joey and his friends look forward to some fresh air and to playing their favorite games.

The left corner of the playground occupies the playing field. Sometimes they play soccer, football, tag, or kickball. They prefer kickball because lots of friends can play the game. Their red rubber ball sails through the air no matter who is up to kick it. Their cheers can be heard a long distance away.

Just as they reach the kickball field, everyone is excited about who will be the captains, and what teams will be formed for the game.

Joey's friend, Eli, runs to the pitcher's mound and declares, "I'm the pitcher for our team!"

"No you're not," yells Jamal, "You were the pitcher yesterday. I want to be the pitcher!"

Joey steps in between Jamal and Eli and calmly says, "Please stop, I don't like that. Arguing about who will pitch the game is wasting our recess time."

Joey continues, "Let's decide by rock, paper, scissor.
Eli, are you ready? Jamal, are you ready?"

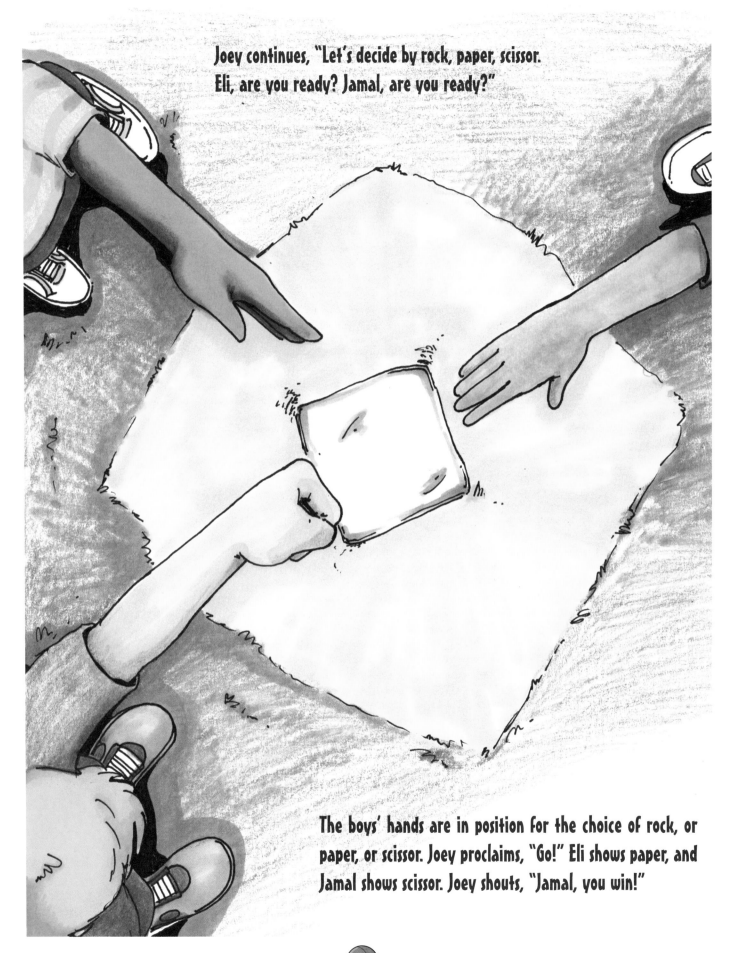

The boys' hands are in position for the choice of rock, or
paper, or scissor. Joey proclaims, "Go!" Eli shows paper, and
Jamal shows scissor. Joey shouts, "Jamal, you win!"

Jamal pitches the ball. Joey's team kicks, scores, and takes the field. Jamal's team takes to offense. They score two runs after eight players kick, but that is all for their fifteen minutes of free time.

The recess bell rings with the game tied 2-2. Joey and his friends walk to line up. Jamal taps Joey on the shoulder and says, "Thanks, Joey. You helped us stop arguing and solved the pitching problem!"

Joey comments back, "You can be part of the problem or part of the solution. Let your friends know that you don't like what is going on by saying, 'Please stop, I don't like that.' It's a way to respectfully stand up for yourself. If you say calmly, 'Please stop, I don't like that,' problems can be worked out easier."

Jamal walks back into class thinking about what Joey said about solving problems. He realizes that saying, 'Please stop, I don't like that,' is a first step to resolve any conflict.

After lunch, Joey and his friends go outside for a thirty-minute recess to continue the tied kickball game. Each team is in position, and the first kicker is at home base.

Joey stands at home base, legs firmly planted for the first pitch. Just as the ball is in motion, Eli yells out, "You can't kick! You're a jerk!"

Joey steps back from home base, turns to Eli, and calmly says, "Please stop, I don't like that. Calling me names is not okay. I would appreciate it if you would stop."

The ball rolls into Eli's hands. He picks it up, and feeling bad about what he said, he turns to Joey, "Sorry, Joey," Eli says apologetically, "I didn't mean to call you a jerk, will you forgive me?"

Eli throws the ball out to the pitcher and replies to Joey, "Thanks for not getting mad at me." Joey exclaims, "Let your friends know that you don't like what is going on by saying, 'Please stop, I don't like that.' It's a way to stand up for yourself. If you can calmly say, 'Please stop, I don't like that,' problems can be worked out easier."

Jamal pitches the ball, and Joey kicks it past third base. He runs to first base. Everyone gets a chance to kick on both teams. Laughter and cheers dominate their play at recess. Pablo yells out, "This is fun!" The girls comment, "Each team scored the same as morning recess. We are tied again!"

You know Joey says, "Recess is a time to have fun and to play together. It doesn't matter if you win or if you lose. We just want to get outside for a break."

The game ends in a 4-4 tie as the noon recess bell rings. As Joey and Eli walk to line up, Eli turns to Joey and says, "You kicked pretty good and you're not a jerk."

Joey replies, "I'm glad we can still be friends."

Eli thinks about what he called Joey. He remembered how he felt when his older brother called him that. He liked how Joey didn't get mad at him but told him nicely to please stop. He walks back into class saying to himself, "I'm going to try really hard to stop being mean to others."

The next day, the playing field was ready for the big game. The freshly mowed grass was perfect for running bases. The sun was shining bright. All the students were eager to get outside for a break.

Joey and his classmates watch the clock anxiously for 10:30 am to come. They look outside and think about yesterday's game. Each one hopes their team is ready.

When the bell rings, they quickly put their books, papers, and pens inside their desks. They walk with power speed to the door and run to the kickball field. With the game tied 4-4, they get in their positions.

Jamal is at the mound ready to pitch the first ball when he turns to first base and yells out, "Hey, girls can't play there."

At those words, Mindy runs over to him and quickly states, "Oh yeah? We played yesterday, and we can play today!"

Jamal crosses his arms and shouts, "Girls stink at kickball, and I don't want my team to lose!"

Mindy glares at him as she rudely announces, "Jamal, you throw like a girl, you're so wimpy!" At these words, Joey steps in between both Jamal and Mindy. Joey calmly says, "Please stop, I don't like that. I don't like it when the two of you talk to each other in that way."

Turning to Mindy, Joey continues, "It's important to let your friends know that you don't like what is going on by saying, 'Please stop, I don't like that.' It's a way to show respect and stand up for yourself. If you calmly say, 'Please stop, I don't like that,' people can work out problems easier."

Jamal remembers that respect earns respect. He realizes that the reason Mindy said those mean things is because he told her that girls stink at kickball. Jamal goes over to Mindy and says, "You really don't stink at kickball. I was just worried the other kids would make fun of me if they saw me playing with girls, I'm sorry."

Mindy apologizes and reminds Jamal that girls are just as capable as boys to play kickball. "Plus," she says, "Jamal, you waste our recess time when you make those comments."

The game continues with Amanda kicking the ball over the head of Jamal and into centerfield. Allison runs after the ball, picks it up, and throws the ball to Pablo on second base. Amanda touches the base as the ball is in the air.

Pablo screams, "You're out, Amanda!" "No, I'm not, Pablo," Amanda says calmly, "I touched the base while the ball was still in the air."

"You're a liar and a snot," Pablo argues.

Amanda tries to stay calm and says, "Please stop, I don't like that. Calling me names is not going to change the fact that I made it to second base before you caught the ball."

All of a sudden, Pablo realizes that she is right, "Okay, okay," he says, "You did make it to base before I caught the ball." I shouldn't have called you names, do you forgive me?"

At this point, Joey walks over to second base and says to Amanda, "Let your friends know that you don't like what is going on by saying, 'Please stop, I don't like that.' It's a way to respectfully stand up for yourself. If you calmly say, 'Please stop, I don't like that,' problems can be worked out easier."

Amanda agrees, "I like that Joey. I will remember to say that next time."

Amanda makes it to home plate just as the recess bell rings. The big game ends with the score 5-4.

Each team congratulates each other for a game that took two days to complete.

Considering the length of the game, Joey and his friends understand that it doesn't matter who wins or who loses. They understand that it's important to play and have fun.

As they walk off the field, Amanda says, "Working things out is much better than fighting. Plus, we have more time to play at recess."

Jamal adds, "Yeh, and remember what we learned in class about RESPECT." We're all friends who like to be together. So, the more we care about each other's feelings, the more fun we have together."

"Having fun is the most important part of recess," Mindy adds, "I like to laugh and to cheer for everybody during kickball."

"Just remember," Joey exclaims, "You have to stand up for yourself. When you say, 'Please stop, I don't like that,' people will listen better and problems can be worked out easier." I look forward to our next recess. How much time before lunch?" he asks.

Everyone yells out, "We have math and social studies, and then it will be lunch recess." They all smile, laugh, and walk back into class.

Follow Up Activities

Ways Parents, Teachers, and Other Adults Can Help Children Learn to be Respectfully Assertive

Writing/Journaling

1. Close your eyes and imagine you did something hurtful to your friend. Your friend gets mad at you and calls you names. How would this make you feel?

2. Now, close your eyes and again imagine you did something hurtful to your friend. Your friend calmly states, "Please stop, I don't like that." How would you react to this statement? How would it make you feel to have your friend say this to you?

Activity 1

In the
story "Please
Stop, I Don't Like That,"
Joey and his friends stood up for
themselves in a respectful way by calmly
saying, "Please stop, I don't like that."

Can you think of five situations where you may
need to use these words?

1. _____

2. _____

3. _____

4. _____

5. _____

As an added activity, role-play / act out these different situations.

Activity 2

It's important to be confident when using the phrase, "Please stop, I don't like that." Circle the ways to be confident when saying these words:

Make Good Eye Contact   Hands Calmly at Your Side

Laughing or Acting Silly   Look at Your Shoes

Hands Waving Around in the Air   Chin Up High

Shoulders Slumped   Firm and Normal Voice

Stand Up Tall   Mean or Harsh Tone

Adult - Child Discussion

It is important for the child to know what to do if the behavior does not stop once he or she says, "Please stop, I don't like that." Talk with the child about when it's appropriate to report the bullying behavior and to whom the child should report.